Conquer Year 6 Science with CGP!

Ready to test the key facts in Year 6 Science? Once pupils have got to grips with all the content in our matching Year 6 Science Knowledge Organiser, they can check how much they've learned with our Knowledge Retriever!

With bonus mixed practice quizzes and a full set of answers too, this book has everything Year 6 pupils need for Science success!

CGP — still the best! ☺

Our sole aim here at CGP is to produce the highest quality books — carefully written, immaculately presented and dangerously close to being funny.

Then we work our socks off to get them out to you — at the cheapest possible prices.

Contents

Published by CGP.

Editors: Josie Gilbert, Jake McGuffie, Luke Molloy and George Wright
Contributors: Paddy Gannon, Philip Goodyear, Tony Laukaitis and Lesley Lockhart

With thanks to Jamie Sinclair for the proofreading.
With thanks to Jan Greenway for the copyright research.

ISBN: 978 1 78908 958 5

Printed by Elanders Ltd, Newcastle upon Tyne.
Clipart from Corel®
Illustrations by: Sandy Gardner Artist, email sandy@sandygardner.co.uk

Based on the classic CGP style created by Richard Parsons.

How to Use This Book

This book is split into different topics that you'll learn about in Year 6 Science. Every page in this book has a matching page in the Year 6 Science **Knowledge Organiser**. Before you fill in the pages in this book, you should have learnt about the topic in your lessons at school and in the Knowledge Organiser.
This is what you need to do:

1 Read the pages and fill in any dotted lines as you go. One dotted line means there's one word missing — sometimes you get given the first letter of the word and sometimes you don't.

2 When you've finished, you can use the answers at the back of the book to check your work. Tick the smiley face to show how well you know the topic.

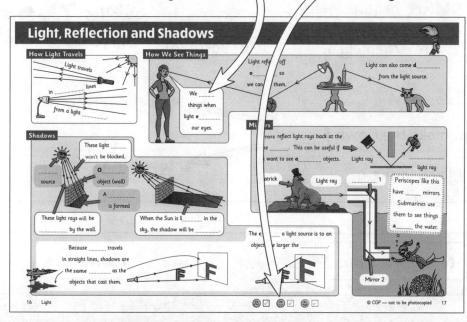

Sometimes you might have used a different word to fill in the gap from what is shown in the answers. That's okay, as long as the word has the same meaning.

There are also **Quizzes** throughout the book:

- These quizzes test content from the previous few pages, including key words. There's also a bigger 'Mixed Quiz' at the end that tests content from the whole book.

- Answers to the quizzes are at the back of the book.
  After you've completed a quiz, mark your answers and write your score in the box at the end of the quiz.

Classification

Reasons for Classification

Classification means putting living things into **g**............ based on the **f**.................. they share.

We classify living things to make them **e**............ to identify and study.

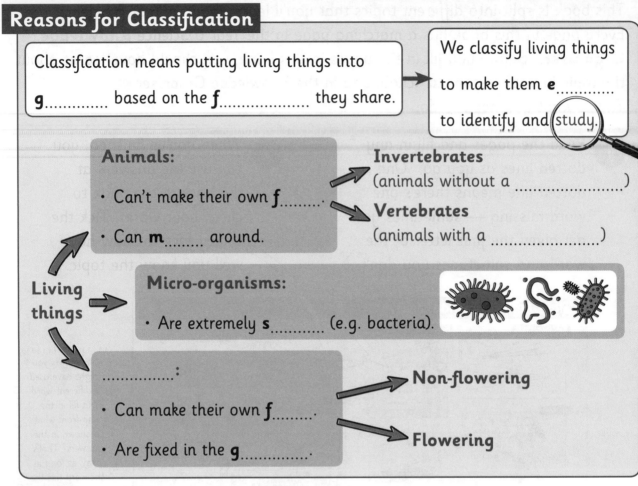

Animals:

- Can't make their own **f**.........
- Can **m**........ around.

Invertebrates
(animals without a ....)

Vertebrates
(animals with a ....)

Micro-organisms:

- Are extremely **s**............ (e.g. bacteria).

Living things

................:

- Can make their own **f**.........
- Are fixed in the **g**...............

Non-flowering

Flowering

Plants

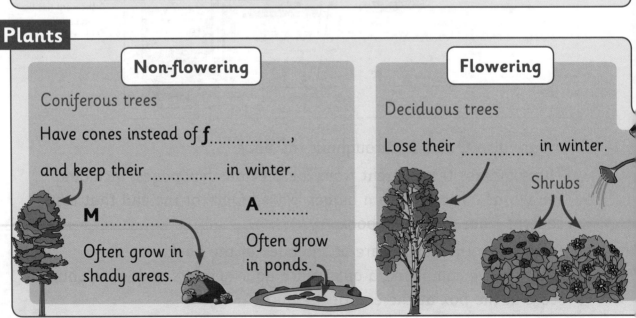

Non-flowering

Coniferous trees

Have cones instead of **f**..................,

and keep their .... in winter.

M................
Often grow in shady areas.

A...........
Often grow in ponds.

Flowering

Deciduous trees

Lose their .... in winter.

Shrubs

Invertebrates

Spiders

.... body parts

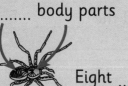

Eight ....

Worms

No l.........

or antennae

Snails and Slugs

S.......... Slimy foot

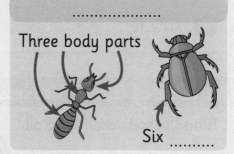

....

Three body parts

Six ....

Vertebrates

....

Breathe with

g.........

Goby

Carp

F....... and scales

Birds

Parrot

W..........

Feathers

Ostrich

Mammals

Mammals give birth to live b....................

Body hair

or f.......

Human Dog

....

Lizard Dry and

scaly ....

Lay eggs Cobra

on ....

Amphibians

Damp ....

These are born with gills, but develop lungs.

Salamander

Lay eggs

in ....

Frog

Cereals

G..................

The Circulatory System

The Circulatory System

The circulatory system is made up of three parts:

1. The **b**..........
2. The **b**.......... **v**...............
3. The **h**..........

The Role of Blood Vessels

Blood vessels are found all over the **b**........, and the blood circulates (travels) **t**............... them.

There are three types of blood vessel:

The Role of the Blood

The blood **c**...............

substances around the ....

Type	Function
Arteries	Carry blood **a**............ from the ....
Veins	Carry blood **b**.......... to the ....
Capillaries	Where substances move .... and **o**...... of the **b**..........

The Role of the Heart

The heart **p**............. blood through the blood **v**...............:

1. Artery carries blood ...... the **l**.........., where it picks up **o**...............

2. Vein brings the blood ....

When the heart beats, it pumps blood out of both arteries.

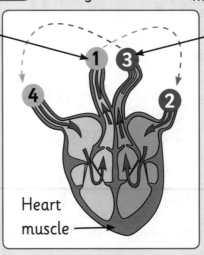

Heart muscle

3. Artery carries blood with **o**.............. to all parts of the ....

4. Vein brings the blood **w**............... oxygen ...., and the cycle repeats.

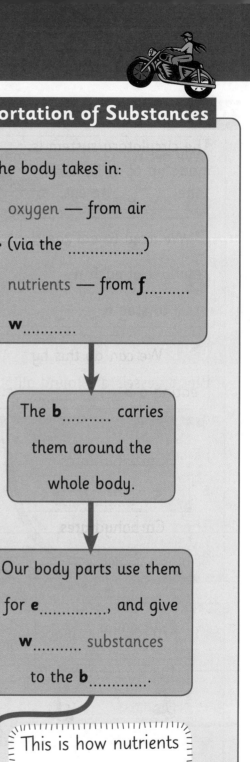

Transportation of Substances

The body takes in:

- oxygen — from air
  (via the ....)
- nutrients — from **f**..........
- **w**............

↓

The **b**.......... carries them around the whole body.

↓

Our body parts use them for **e**..............., and give **w**.......... substances to the **b**..............

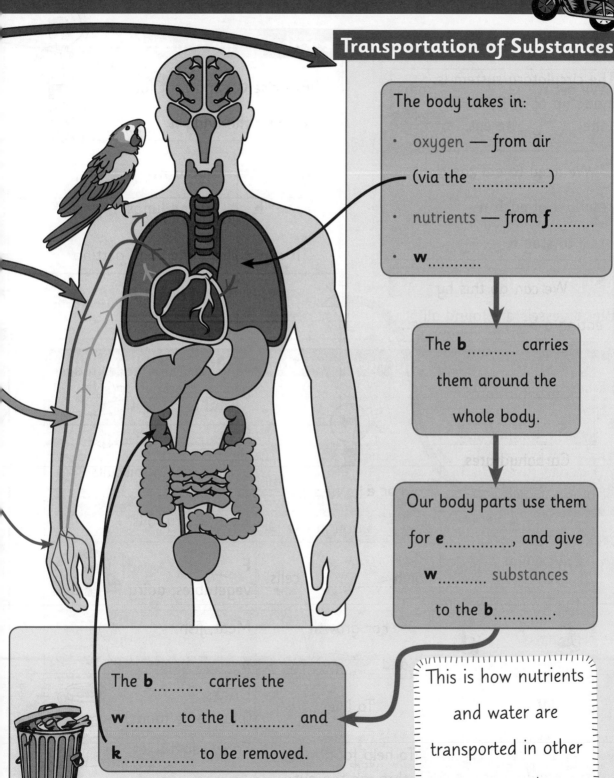

The **b**.......... carries the **w**.......... to the **l**............. and **k**................ to be removed.

This is how nutrients and water are transported in other **a**................. too.

Diet, Exercise and Drugs

Diet

We get **n**.................. from the .... we eat.

We need to eat the right amount of each **n**.................. to stay **h**...............

We can do this by eating a **b**.................. diet.

Exercise

Exercise is important for keeping the body **h**...............

It strengthens your **m**.................., **h**........... and lungs.

It can prevent the body getting fat by using up **f**......... for energy.

Nutrients	Why they're needed	Which foods have them
Carbohydrates (**S**..................)	For **e**..............	Bread, pasta, **p**..................
Carbohydrates (Sugars)		Sweets, cakes, biscuits
....		Meat, dairy, oils
Vitamins and	For **h**.................. cells.	**F**.............., vegetables, dairy
Proteins	For growth and	Meat, fish, **n**........., beans
W...........	To live.	Drinks (plus some foods)
....	To help food move through the gut.	Fruit, vegetables, wholegrain **b**...........

It improves your co-ordination.

It can help you .... at night.

How regular exercise helps the body

Drugs are **d**........................ if misused.

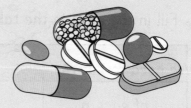

They can be **a**...................., and can cause a lot of damage to the **b**.......... and body.

Alcohol

Can **r**........... blood pressure

Can damage the liver, **h**........... and stomach

S........... your reactions

Solvents

Can cause **b**.......... damage

They are addictive

Solvents are chemicals commonly found in everyday products, such as paint and glue.

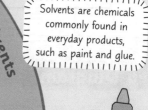

Tobacco contains nicotine, which is **a**....................

Can cause **h**........... attacks, blocked arteries, **c**............... and breathing issues

Smoking

Animals, Plants & Healthy Living Quiz

Do you know your veins from your vertebrates? Try this quiz to find out...

Key Words

1. Fill in the gaps in the table below.

Word	Definition
Classification	....
Capillary	....
....	A drug that's found in some drinks like wine and beer.

3 marks

Key Diagrams

2. Complete the labels to show the four different blood vessels of the heart.

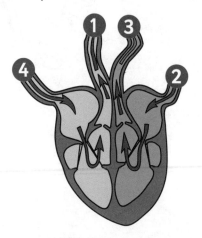

1 Artery to the lungs.

2 .... from the ....

3 .... to all parts

of the ....

4 .... from the body.

5 marks

3. We can keep our bodies healthy by eating a balanced diet, getting plenty of exercise, and avoiding health risks.

    a) Why are proteins needed in the body?

    ....

    b) What is one benefit of exercising regularly?

    ....

    c) What is one harmful effect smoking can have on the body?

    ....

    _____
    3 marks

4. Insects and spiders can be grouped based on their similarities and differences.

    a) Give one similarity between insects and spiders.

    ....

    b) Give one difference between insects and spiders.

    ....

    _____
    2 marks

5. Fill in the gaps to describe how plants are classified.

    Plants are .... things which can make

    their own ...., and are fixed in the ....

    Different plants can be put into one of two groups:

    flowering or ....

    _____
    4 marks

Score: [   ]

Variation and Adaptations

Variation

Animals and plants produce

o........................ of the same kind.

Usually the offspring look ....,

but not identical, to their parents.

Father:

brown eyes

We look like our p................

because we .... some

characteristics from them.

Daughter:

.... eyes

Adaptations

Animals and plants can develop

.... (special features)

to suit the place they live in.

A.......................... help living things

s............... in their environment.

Animal Adaptations — Examples

Name: ....

Environment: South Pole (cold, wet, icy)

webbed f.......... help them swim

We look different to our .... because we have some characteristics that

are .... from them. These differences are called v......................

Mother

Father

Son

different
hair shade

different
face shape

For example, animals living in or near a pond might have developed features like:

c........................ to help them hide in the reeds

flippers or fins to move around q.............. in the water

gills to breathe ....

rounded body shape reduces .... loss

don't produce much wee or sweat to save ....

layer of body fat keeps them ....

big feet to stop them sinking into the ....

Name: Camel

Environment: .... (hot, dry, sandy)

sandy colour for c...........................

Plant Adaptations — Examples

Name: ....

Environment: Desert (hot, dry, sandy)

thin needle leaves don't lose ....

fleshy stems store ....

l.......... roots find water

Name: Moth Orchid

Environment: **J**............ (hot, wet, humid)

waxy, waterproof l............... to avoid rot

bright f................ to attract insects

Evolution

How Living Things Evolve

Evolution is how living things .... over time:

1 Living things vary — they are .... from each other.

2 Those that are better **a**.................. to their habitat are more likely to **s**.................. and **r**...................

4 Over time, more and more of the living things will have the **f**.................. that make them well-adapted to their **h**...................

3 Many of the **o**.................. will **i**.................. the useful adaptations.

Example: How Giraffes Evolved

1 A long time ago, a group of giraffe-like **a**.................. existed. Some had longer .... than others.

2 The animals with longer .... could reach more leaves to **e**........, so were more likely to **s**.................. and have babies.

Fossils

Fossils are the **s**.............. of long **d**........ plants and animals that can be found in **r**...........

Plants and animals around today look .... from those that were around millions of **y**............ ago. This is because they have **e**.............. over time.

Fossils can show us what some plants and .... used to **l**........ like.

E.g.:

fossil   animal
alive today

The **f**............ shows that the animal alive today has **e**.............. to have longer **l**........ and a more rounded body.

3 Many of the babies **i**..................... their parents' .... necks, which helped them to **s**.............. too.

4 This process carried on until eventually the animals had **e**................ into giraffes, which all have **l**........ **n**............

Evolution and Inheritance Quiz

Millions of years of evolution have led up to you taking this quiz — good luck...

Key Words

1. Fill in the gaps in the table below.

Word	Definition
....	A characteristic of an organism that helps it to survive in its habitat.
....	Differences between living things.
Evolution	....
Fossil	....

4 marks

Now Try These

2. Fill in the gaps in these sentences about fossils.

Fossils can show us what some plants and animals used to

.... like. Plants and animals around today look

.... from those that were around millions of

years ago. This is because they have ....

3 marks

3. Write down whether each statement is true or false.

There is variation in living things because offspring don't inherit any characteristics from their parents. ....

Living things produce offspring of the same kind. ....

_____
2 marks

4. For each animal, describe an adaptation it has and explain how it helps them survive in their environment.

a) A penguin living in the South Pole.

....

b) A camel living in the desert.

....

_____
2 marks

5. Number these steps from 1-4, with 1 being the first step and 4 being the last, to put the description of how animals evolve in the correct order.

| Many of these animals' offspring will inherit the useful adaptations. | .... |

| Eventually all the animals in the group will have the useful adaptations. | .... |

| Animals in a group vary — they are different from each other. | .... |

| The animals in the group that are better adapted to their habitat are more likely to survive and reproduce. | .... |

_____
3 marks

Score:

Light, Reflection and Shadows

How Light Travels

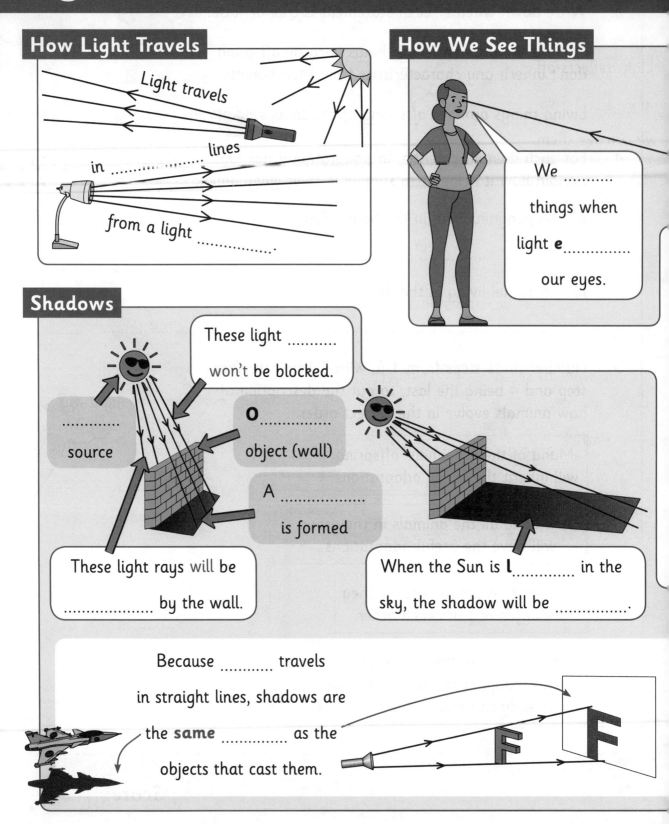

Light travels

in .... lines

from a light ....

How We See Things

We ....

things when

light **e**...............

our eyes.

Shadows

These light ....

won't **be** blocked.

....

source

O................

object (wall)

A ....

is formed

These light rays **will be**

.... by the wall.

When the Sun is **l**............. in the

sky, the shadow will be ....

Because .... travels

in straight lines, shadows are

the **same** .... as the

objects that cast them.

16   Light

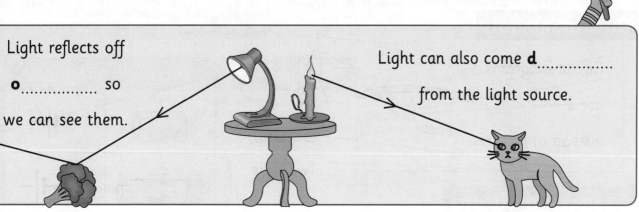

Light reflects off

o.............. so

we can see them.

Light can also come **d**..............

from the light source.

Mirrors

Mirrors reflect light rays back at the

same .... This can be useful if

you want to see **a**.............. objects.

Light ray

Patrick

Light ray

.... light ray

.... 1

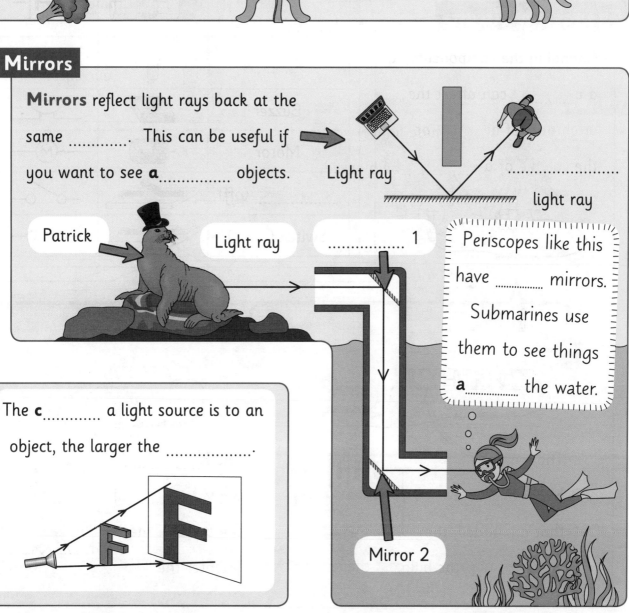

Periscopes like this

have .... mirrors.

Submarines use

them to see things

a.............. the water.

The **c**............. a light source is to an

object, the larger the ....

Mirror 2

Circuits and Components

Circuit Symbols

Electricity can be very dangerous, so you need to work safely with it. E.g. never use electricity near water.

Circuit diagrams use **s**.................. instead of pictures.

Component	Picture	Symbol
C......... (battery)	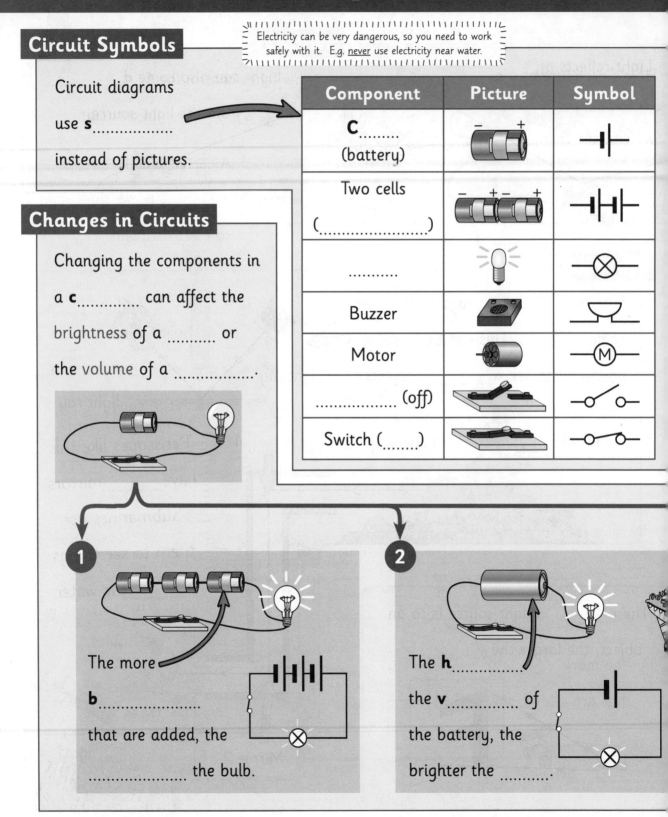	
Two cells (.....................)		
....		
Buzzer		
Motor		
.... (off)		
Switch (.......)		

Changes in Circuits

Changing the components in a **c**.............. can affect the brightness of a .... or the volume of a ....

1 The more **b**...................... that are added, the .... the bulb.

2 The **h**................ the **v**................ of the battery, the brighter the ....

18   Electricity

Here's a picture of a **c**.............:

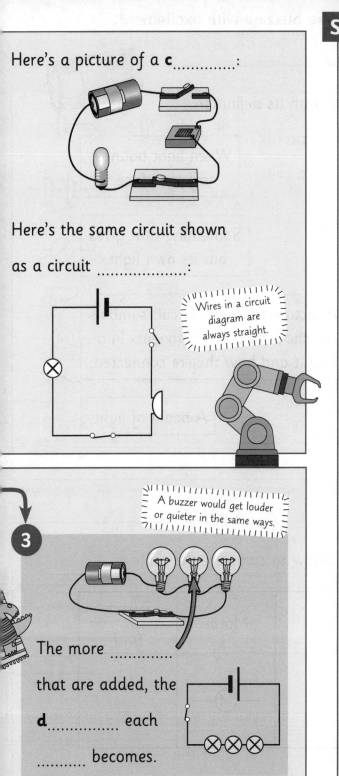

Here's the same circuit shown

as a circuit ....:

Wires in a circuit diagram are always straight.

3

A buzzer would get louder or quieter in the same ways.

The more ....

that are added, the

d.............. each

.... becomes.

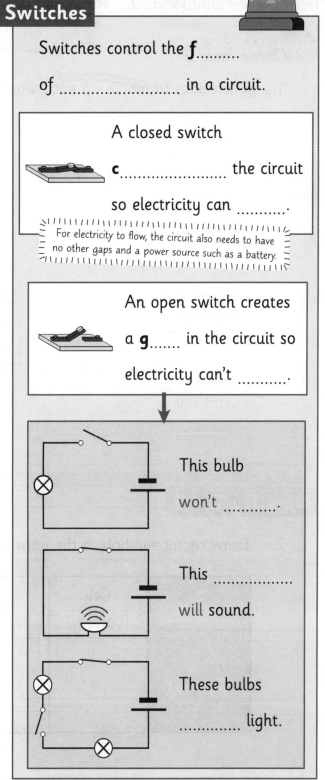

Switches control the **f**..........

of .... in a circuit.

A closed switch

c......................... the circuit

so electricity can ....

For electricity to flow, the circuit also needs to have no other gaps and a power source such as a battery.

An open switch creates

a **g**....... in the circuit so

electricity can't ....

This bulb

won't ....

This ....

will **sound**.

These bulbs

.... light.

Light and Electricity Quiz

Here comes another quiz... Hopefully you're buzzing with excitement.

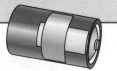

1. Draw lines to match up each word with its definition.

Light source		When light bounces off a surface.

Circuit diagram — Something that gives out its own light.

Reflection — A picture that uses circuit symbols to show all the components in a circuit and how they're connected.

Light ray — A beam of light.

3 marks

Now Try These

2. Draw circuit symbols in the gaps below to complete the table.

Component	Cell (battery)	Bulb	Motor	Switch (on)
Symbol			—(M)—	

3 marks

3. Write down whether each of these sentences is true or false.

a) Light travels in straight lines. ....

b) Mirrors reflect light rays back at the same angle. ....

c) A buzzer will sound in a circuit with
an open switch. ....

3 marks

4. Complete these sentences about how components in
a circuit can affect the brightness of a bulb.

a) The more batteries that are added,

the .... the bulb.

b) The more bulbs that are added,

the .... each bulb becomes.

c) The .... the voltage of

the battery, the brighter the bulb.

3 marks

5. Fill in the gaps to describe how we see things.

We see things when .... enters

our eyes. Light can either .... off

an object and into our eyes, or enter our

eyes directly from a light ....

3 marks

6. Circle the correct option to complete the sentence.

An object's shadow is the same shape as the **object / light source**.

1 mark

Score:

Working Scientifically

Planning an Experiment

1 Write down the .... you want to answer.

2 Write a .... for the experiment. This should include:

- what you will **m**................. /observe,
- what **e**..................... you will use,
- how you will make it a .... test.

To make an experiment **f**......., change one **v**................. at a time and keep everything else the ....

(A **v**................. is anything that could affect your results.)

Patterns in Results

Your .... may form a pattern. E.g.:

Distance (cm)	Width of shadow (cm)
20	19
40	20
60	24
80	21

Results that don't fit the .... might suggest that a **m**................. has been made in your experiment.

If possible, **r**................. your .... a few times to make sure your results are **r**................. .

Displaying Results

Think about how best to display your ....

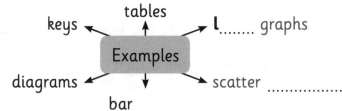

keys ← tables → **l**........ graphs

Examples

diagrams ← → scatter ....

bar ....

The best way depends on your **e**................. .

Conclusions

Your experiment should end with a .... — a sentence that sums up your **f**................. .

The sentence is usually written like: 'As one thing changes like this, another thing changes like this.' You could back this up by using examples from your results.

3 Make a p....................
(what you think will happen).

Line Graphs

Plot your results on a grid, then j............
them up with .... lines.

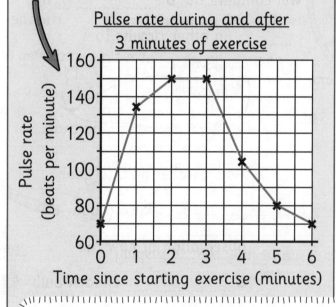

Pulse rate during and after
3 minutes of exercise

Pulse rate (beats per minute) — y-axis: 60, 80, 100, 120, 140, 160

Time since starting exercise (minutes) — x-axis: 0 1 2 3 4 5 6

Line graphs are often used to show how
something c................ over ....

Explain whether there were any

P................ with your experiment:

• Did you make any m............?

• Did all the results fit with the ....?

• Could the test have been .... fair?

Scatter Graphs

Plot your results on a grid,
then draw one .... that
goes as c.......... to all the
p............. as possible.

Width of an object's shadow
for different distances
between the object and screen

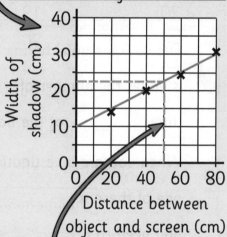

Width of shadow (cm) — y-axis: 0, 10, 20, 30, 40

Distance between
object and screen (cm) — x-axis: 0 20 40 60 80

By drawing from the x-axis to the line,
then across to the y-axis, you can predict the width
of the shadow for different distances, e.g.: 'The
shadow will be 23 cm wide at a distance of 50 cm.'

P............................ with the
experiment might mean your
results are not r.........................
— if so, you might want to
do further t.............. .

Investigation – Changing Circuits

Planning your Experiment

1 What question do you want to answer?

How does the number of bulbs or the voltage of a battery affect the brightness of bulbs in a circuit?

2 How will you do your experiment?

1. Make the .... shown below and observe the brightness of the .... This is the original circuit that you will compare the **b**........................ of .... in other circuits to.

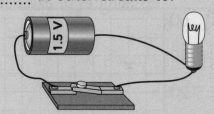

- The variable you change each time is either the number of .... or the **v**............... of the battery.

- When you are investigating one of these **v**....................., you need to **c**............... all the other **v**.....................

- The variable you **o**................. is the brightness of the bulb (or bulbs).

2. Add another bulb to your .... Record your observation of how the **b**........................ of each bulb changes in your results table.

You could change the circuit back and forth with the original to make your comparison of the brightness more accurate.

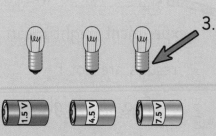

3. Repeat step 2 for the different changes to the .... that you're investigating — adding different numbers of .... and changing the **v**............... of the battery.

Results

Change to original circuit	Observations compared to original circuit
1 extra bulb added	each bulb is **d**_____
2 extra bulbs added	each bulb is **d**_____ — bulbs are a bit **d**_____ than when 1 extra bulb was added
3 extra bulbs added	each bulb is **d**_____ — bulbs are a bit **d**_____ than when 2 extra bulbs were added
1.5 V **b**_____ changed to 4.5 V	bulb is quite a lot _____ than before
1.5 V **b**_____ changed to 7.5 V	bulb was very bright for a moment, then went out

You might come up with further predictions based on your results, which you could test by doing another experiment. E.g. you might predict that to make the bulb brighter, you could add more batteries instead of using a more powerful one.

This result doesn't fit with the pattern — you might want to **r**_____ the experiment to see if it happens again.

3 **What do you predict will happen?**

Increasing the number of _____ in the circuit will reduce the brightness of each bulb, but increasing the _____ of the battery will increase the brightness.

Conclusion

The results show:

- the _____ bulbs there are, the dimmer each bulb is.

- the higher the **v**_____ of the battery, the _____ the bulb is.

Mixed Quiz

You know the drill by now. Let's get quizzing...

1. Fill in the gaps in the table below.

Word	Definition
....	A dark area made when light rays are blocked by an object.
Vertebrate	....
....	The red liquid that transports nutrients, water and oxygen around the body, as well as waste products.
Prediction	....
....	Something that does a job in a circuit, e.g. a bulb or a buzzer.
Balanced diet	....
....	A substance found in cigarettes and cigars. It contains nicotine, which is addictive. Smoking it can cause health problems.

7 marks

2. Draw lines to match up each word with its definition.

| Characteristic | | A factor in an experiment that you can control, change or measure. |

| Offspring | | A substance that changes how the body works. |

| Variable | | A feature of an organism. |

| Drug | | The children of a living thing. |

3. Use words from the box to complete the definitions below.
You won't need to use all of the words.

blood	fossil	living	inheritance
parent	heart	circulatory	micro

a) ....-organism: an extremely small

.... thing, e.g. bacteria.

b) ....: when characteristics get

passed on from a .... to its offspring.

c) .... system: the system that transports

substances around the body in the ....

4. The diagram below labels each type of blood vessel in the body. Complete the labels by naming the blood vessels.

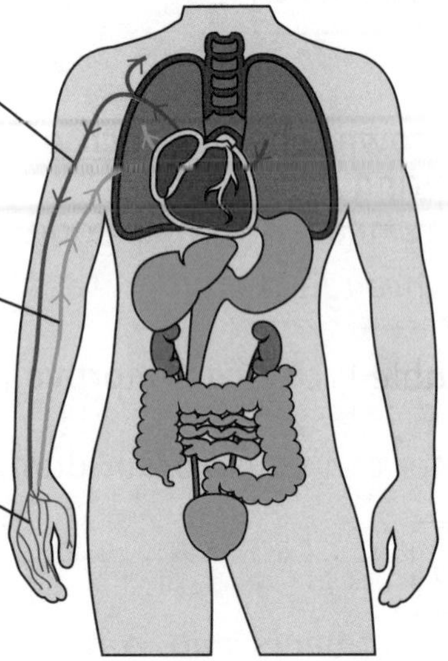

..............................: carries

blood away from the heart.

..............................: carries

blood back to the heart.

..............................: where substances

move in and out of the blood.

_____

3 marks

Now Try These

5. Circle the correct word to complete the sentence.

   Switches / motors can control the flow of electricity in a circuit.

   _____

   1 mark

6. Fill in the gaps below to describe how shadows change size.

   The closer a .... source is to an object,

   the .... the object's shadow.

   _____

   2 marks

7. On what type of graph do you plot your results on a grid and then join the results up with straight lines?

   ....

   _____

   1 mark

8. What word is used to describe the difference in characteristics between offspring and their parents?

....

1 mark

9. Write down whether each of these sentences is true or false.

Fats are needed to help food
move through the gut.   ....

Regular exercise can improve your co-ordination.   ....

Solvents can cause brain damage.   ....

3 marks

10. Millions of years ago, a group of giraffe-like animals existed.
They ate leaves on trees to survive.
Some of the animals had longer necks than others.
Explain why the animals with longer necks were more likely to
survive than the other animals.

....

....

....

1 mark

11. The five vertebrate groups are **fish**, **birds**, **mammals**, **reptiles**
and **amphibians**. Which vertebrate group would an animal be
classified in if it had...

a) body hair or fur?   ....

b) wings and feathers?   ....

c) gills, fins and scales?   ....

3 marks

12. Fill in the gaps below to describe how substances
    are transported in the body.

    The blood carries .... (from the air), ...

    (from food) and water all around the body. Our body parts use

    them, and produce .... substances. The blood carries

    these substances to the .... and kidneys to be removed.

    _____
    4 marks

13. Adaptations are features that help living things
    survive in their environment.
    Describe two ways that cactuses are adapted to
    surviving in the desert.

    1. ....

    ....

    2. ....

    ....

    _____
    2 marks

14. Write down three different ways you could
    display the results of an experiment.

    1. ....

    2. ....

    3. ....

    _____
    3 marks

15. What does tobacco contain that makes it addictive?

    ....

    _____
    1 mark

16. Fill in the gaps below about mirrors.

Light rays travel in .... lines, and mirrors reflect light

rays back at the same .... Mirrors can be useful for

seeing .... objects — for example, submarines use

.... (which have two mirrors) to see above water.

4 marks

17. Describe two key differences between plants and animals.

1. ....

....

2. ....

....

2 marks

18. For each change described below, write down whether the
bulb in the circuit will become **brighter** or **dimmer**.

a) The battery is replaced with one
that has a higher voltage.   ....

b) More batteries are added.   ....

c) More bulbs are added.   ....

3 marks

Score:

Answers

Pages 2-3 — Classification

Reasons for Classification

Classification means putting living things into **groups** based on the **features** they share.

We classify living things to make them **easier** to identify and study.

Animals:
- Can't make their own **food**.
- Can **move** around.

Invertebrates
(animals without a **backbone**)

Vertebrates
(animals with a **backbone**)

Micro-organisms:
- Are extremely **small** (e.g. bacteria).

Plants:
- Can make their own **food**.
- Are fixed in the **ground**.

Non-flowering

Flowering

Plants

Non-flowering:

Coniferous trees
Have cones instead of **flowers**, and keep their **leaves** in winter.

Mosses
Often grow in shady areas.

Algae
Often grow in ponds.

Flowering:

Deciduous trees
Lose their **leaves** in winter.

Shrubs

Cereals

Grasses

Invertebrates

Spiders
Two body parts
Eight **legs**

Worms
No **legs** or antennae

Snails and Slugs
Shell
Slimy foot

Insects
Three body parts
Six **legs**

Vertebrates

Fish
Breathe with **gills**
Fins and scales

Birds
Wings
Feathers

Mammals
Body hair or **fur**
Mammals give birth to live **babies**.

Reptiles
Dry and scaly **skin**
Lay eggs on **land**

Amphibians
Damp **skin**
Lay eggs in **water**

Pages 4-5 — The Circulatory System

The Circulatory System

1. The **blood**
2. The **blood vessels**
3. The **heart**

The Role of the Blood

The blood **carries** substances around the **body**.

The Role of Blood Vessels

Blood vessels are found all over the **body**, and the blood circulates (travels) **through** them.

Arteries	Carry blood **away** from the **heart**
Veins	Carry blood **back** to the **heart**.
Capillaries	Where substances move **in** and **out** of the **blood**.

The Role of the Heart

The heart **pumps** blood through the blood **vessels**:

1. Artery carries blood **to the lungs**, where it picks up **oxygen**.
2. Vein brings the blood **back**.
3. Artery carries blood with **oxygen** to all parts of the **body**.
4. Vein brings the blood **without** oxygen **back**, and the cycle repeats.

Transportation of Substances

The body takes in:
- oxygen — from air (via the **lungs**)
- nutrients — from **food**
- **water**

The **blood** carries them around the whole body.

Our body parts use them for **energy**, and give **waste** substances to the **blood**.

The **blood** carries the **waste** to the **lungs** and **kidneys** to be removed.

This is how nutrients and water are transported in other **animals** too.

Answers

Pages 6-7 — Diet, Exercise and Drugs

Diet

We get **nutrients** from the **food** we eat.

We need to eat the right amount of each **nutrient** to stay **healthy**.

We can do this by eating a **balanced** diet.

Carbohydrates (**Starches**) — For **energy**.
Bread, pasta, **potatoes**

Carbohydrates (Sugars) — For **energy**.
Sweets, cakes, biscuits

Fats — For **energy**.
Meat, dairy, oils

Vitamins and **Minerals** — For **healthy** cells.
Fruit, vegetables, dairy

Proteins — For growth and **repair**.
Meat, fish, **nuts**, beans

Water — To live.
Drinks (plus some foods)

Fibre — To help food move through the gut.
Fruit, vegetables, wholegrain **bread**

Exercise

Exercise is important for keeping the body **healthy**.

How regular exercise helps the body:
It strengthens your **muscles**, **heart** and lungs.
It can prevent the body getting fat by using up **food** for energy.
It improves your co-ordination.
It can help you **sleep** at night.

Drugs

Drugs are **dangerous** if misused.

They can be **addictive**, and can cause a lot of damage to the **brain** and body.

Alcohol:
Can **raise** blood pressure
Can damage the liver, **heart** and stomach
Slows your reactions

Solvents:
Can cause **brain** damage
They are addictive

Smoking:
Tobacco contains nicotine, which is **addictive**
Can cause **heart** attacks, blocked arteries, **cancer** and breathing issues

Pages 8-9 — Animals, Plants & Healthy Living Quiz

Key Words

1. Classification — **When living things are put into groups based on their features.**
   Capillary — **A blood vessel where substances move in and out of the blood.**
   Alcohol — A drug that's found in some drinks like wine and beer. (3 marks)

Key Diagrams

2. 1. Artery to the lungs.
   2. **Vein** from the **lungs**.
   3. **Artery** to all parts of the **body**.
   4. **Vein** from the body.
   (5 marks)

Now Try These

3. a) **For growth and repair** (1 mark)
   b) E.g. **it strengthens your muscles, heart and lungs / it can prevent the body from getting fat / it improves your co-ordination / it can help you sleep at night.** (1 mark)
   c) E.g. **it can cause heart attacks / blocked arteries / cancer / breathing issues.** (1 mark)

4. a) E.g. **they don't have backbones / they are invertebrates.** (1 mark)
   b) E.g. **they have different numbers of legs / they have different numbers of body parts.** (1 mark)

5. Plants are **living** things which can make their own **food**, and are fixed in the **ground**. Different plants can be put into one of two groups: flowering or **non-flowering**. (4 marks)

Answers

Pages 10-11 — Variation and Adaptations

Variation

Animals and plants produce **offspring** of the same kind. Usually the offspring look **similar**, but not identical, to their parents.

Father: brown eyes
We look like our **parents** because we **inherit** some characteristics from them.
Daughter: **brown** eyes

We look different to our **parents** because we have some characteristics that are **different** from them. These differences are called **variation**.

Adaptations

Animals and plants can develop **adaptations** (special features) to suit the place they live in. **Adaptations** help living things **survive** in their environment.

For example, animals living in or near a pond might have developed features like:
camouflage to help them hide in the reeds
flippers or fins to move around **quickly** in the water
gills to breathe **underwater**

Animal Adaptations — Examples

Name: **Penguin**
Environment: South Pole (cold, wet, icy)
webbed **feet** help them swim
rounded body shape reduces **heat** loss
layer of body fat keeps them **warm**
Name: Camel
Environment: **Desert** (hot, dry, sandy)
don't produce much wee or sweat to save **water**
big feet to stop them sinking into the **sand**
sandy colour for **camouflage**

Plant Adaptations — Examples

Name: Moth Orchid
Environment: **Jungle** (hot, wet, humid)
waxy, waterproof **leaves** to avoid rot
bright **flowers** to attract insects
Name: **Cactus**
Environment: Desert (hot, dry, sandy)
thin needle leaves don't lose **water**
fleshy stems store **water**
long roots find water

Pages 12-13 — Evolution

How Living Things Evolve

Evolution is how living things **change** over time:

1) Living things vary — they are **different** from each other.

2) Those that are better **adapted** to their habitat are more likely to **survive** and **reproduce**.

3) Many of the **offspring** will **inherit** the useful adaptations.

4) Over time, more and more of the living things will have the **features** that make them well-adapted to their **habitat**.

Example: How Giraffes Evolved

1) A long time ago, a group of giraffe-like **animals** existed. Some had longer **necks** than others.

2) The animals with longer **necks** could reach more leaves to **eat**, so were more likely to **survive** and have babies.

3) Many of the babies **inherited** their parents' **longer** necks, which helped them to **survive** too.

4) This process carried on until eventually the animals had **evolved** into giraffes, which all have **long necks**.

Answers

Fossils

Fossils are the **shapes** of long **dead** plants and animals that can be found in **rocks**.

Plants and animals around today look **different** from those that were around millions of **years** ago. This is because they have **evolved** over time.

Fossils can show us what some plants and **animals** used to **look** like.

The **fossil** shows that the animal alive today has **evolved** to have longer **legs** and a more rounded body.

Pages 14-15 — Evolution and Inheritance Quiz

Key Words

1. **Adaptation** — A characteristic of an organism that helps it to survive in its habitat.
   Variation — Differences between living things.
   Evolution — **How living things change over time.**
   Fossil — **The shape of a long dead animal or plant, found in a rock.**
   (4 marks)

Now Try These

2. Fossils can show us what some plants and animals used to **look** like. Plants and animals around today look **different** from those that were around millions of years ago. This is because they have **evolved**. (3 marks)

3. **False**
   True (2 marks)

4. a) E.g. **they have rounded bodies to reduce heat loss / they have webbed feet to help them swim / they have a layer of body fat that keeps them warm** (1 mark)

   b) E.g. **they have sandy coloured fur for camouflage / they don't produce much wee or sweat to save water / they have big feet to stop them sinking into the sand** (1 mark)

5. Many of these animals' offspring will inherit the useful adaptations. — **3**
   Eventually all the animals in the group will have the useful adaptations. — **4**
   Animals in a group vary — they are different from each other. — **1**
   The animals in the group that are better adapted to their habitat will be more likely to survive and reproduce. — **2**
   (3 marks for all answers correct, otherwise 2 marks for at least two answers correct or 1 mark for one answer correct)

Pages 16-17 — Light, Reflection and Shadows

How Light Travels

Light travels in **straight** lines from a light **source**.

How We See Things

We **see** things when light **enters** our eyes.
Light reflects off **objects** so we can see them.
Light can also come **directly** from the light source.

Shadows

These light **rays** won't be blocked.
Light source
Opaque object (wall)
A **shadow** is formed
These light rays will be **blocked** by the wall.

When the Sun is **lower** in the sky, the shadow will be **longer**.

Because **light** travels in straight lines, shadows are the same **shape** as the objects that cast them.
The **closer** a light source is to an object, the larger the **shadow**.

Mirrors

Mirrors reflect light rays back at the same **angle**. This can be useful if you want to see **around** objects.

Light ray
Reflected light ray

Light ray
Mirror 1
Mirror 2

Periscopes like this have **two** mirrors. Submarines use them to see things **above** the water.

Answers

Pages 18-19 — Circuits and Components

Circuit Symbols

Circuit diagrams use **symbols** instead of pictures.

Cell (battery)
Two cells (**batteries**)
Bulb
Buzzer
Motor
Switch (off)
Switch (**on**)

Here's a picture of a **circuit**:
Here's the same circuit shown as a circuit **diagram**:

Changes in Circuits

Changing the components in a **circuit** can affect the brightness of a **bulb** or the volume of a **buzzer**.

1. The more **batteries** that are added, the **brighter** the bulb.

2. The **higher** the **voltage** of the battery, the brighter the **bulb**.

3. The more **bulbs** that are added, the **dimmer** each **bulb** becomes.

Switches

Switches control the **flow** of **electricity** in a circuit.

A closed switch **completes** the circuit so electricity can **flow**.

An open switch creates a **gap** in the circuit so electricity can't **flow**.

This bulb won't **light**.
This **buzzer** will sound.
These bulbs **won't** light.

Pages 20-21 — Light and Electricity Quiz

Key Words

1. Light source — **Something that gives out its own light.**
Circuit diagram — **A picture that uses circuit symbols to show all the components in a circuit and how they're connected.**
Reflection — **When light bounces off a surface.**
Light ray — **A beam of light.**
(3 marks for all lines drawn correctly, otherwise 2 marks for at least two lines drawn correctly and 1 mark for one line drawn correctly)

Now Try These

2. Cell (battery):
Bulb:
Switch (on):
(3 marks)

3. a) **True** (1 mark)
   b) **True** (1 mark)
   c) **False** (1 mark)

4. a) The more batteries that are added, the **brighter** the bulb. (1 mark)
   b) The more bulbs that are added, the **dimmer** each bulb becomes. (1 mark)
   c) The **higher** the voltage of the battery, the brighter the bulb. (1 mark)

5. We see things when **light** enters our eyes. Light can either **reflect** off an object and into our eyes, or enter our eyes directly from a light **source**. (3 marks)

6. An object's shadow is the same shape as the **object**. (1 mark)

Pages 22-23 — Working Scientifically

Planning an Experiment

1. Write down the **question** you want to answer.

2. Write a **method** for the experiment. This should include:
   - what you will **measure**/observe,
   - what **equipment** you will use,
   - how you will make it a **fair** test.

To make an experiment **fair**, change one **variable** at a time and keep everything else the **same**.
(A **variable** is anything that could affect your results.)

3. Make a **prediction** (what you think will happen).

Patterns in Results

Your **results** may form a pattern.

Results that don't fit the **pattern** might suggest that a **mistake** has been made in your experiment.

If possible, **repeat** your **experiment** a few times to make sure your results are **reliable**.

Answers

Displaying Results

Think about how best to display your **results**.

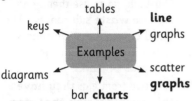

tables

keys

line graphs

Examples

diagrams

scatter **graphs**

bar **charts**

The best way depends on your **experiment**.

Line Graphs

Plot your results on a grid, then **join** them up with **straight** lines.

Line graphs are often used to show how something **changes** over **time**.

Scatter Graphs

Plot your results on a grid, then draw one **line** that goes as **close** to all the **points** as possible.

Conclusions

Your experiment should end with a **conclusion** — a sentence that sums up your **findings**.

Explain whether there were any **problems** with your experiment:

- Did you make any **mistakes**?
- Did all the results fit with the **pattern**?
- Could the test have been **more** fair?

Problems with the experiment might mean your results are not **reliable** — if so, you might want to do further **tests**.

Pages 24-25 — Investigation — Changing Circuits

Planning your Experiment

How will you do your experiment?

1. Make the **circuit** shown below and observe the brightness of the **bulb**. This is the original circuit that you will compare the **brightness** of **bulbs** in other circuits to.

2. Add another bulb to your **circuit**. Record your observation of how the **brightness** of each bulb changes in your results table.

3. Repeat step 2 for the different changes to the **circuit** that you're investigating — adding different numbers of **bulbs** and changing the **voltage** of the battery.

- The variable you change each time is either the number of **bulbs** or the **voltage** of the battery.
- When you are investigating one of these **variables**, you need to **control** all the other **variables**.
- The variable you **observe** is the brightness of the bulb (or bulbs)

What do you predict will happen?

Increasing the number of **bulbs** in the circuit will reduce the brightness of each bulb, but increasing the **voltage** of the battery will increase the brightness.

Results

Table:

1 extra bulb added → each bulb is **dimmer**

2 extra bulbs added → each bulb is **dimmer** — bulbs are a bit **dimmer** than when 1 extra bulb was added

3 extra bulbs added → each bulb is **dimmer** — bulbs are a bit **dimmer** than when 2 extra bulbs were added

1.5 V **battery** changed to 4.5 V → bulb is quite a lot **brighter** than before

1.5 V **battery** changed to 7.5 V → bulb was very bright for a moment, then went out

This result doesn't fit with the pattern — you might want to **repeat** the experiment to see if it happens again.

Conclusion

The results show:

- the **more** bulbs there are, the dimmer each bulb is.
- the higher the **voltage** of the battery, the **brighter** the bulb is.

Answers

Pages 26-31 — Mixed Quiz

Key Words

1. **Shadow** — A dark area made when light rays are blocked by an object.
   Vertebrate — **An animal with a backbone**.
   Blood — The red liquid that transports nutrients, water and oxygen around the body, as well as waste products.
   Prediction — **What you think will happen in an experiment**.
   Component — Something that does a job in a circuit, e.g. a bulb or a buzzer.
   Balanced diet — **This means eating the right amount of different nutrients to stay healthy.**
   Tobacco — A substance found in cigarettes and cigars. It contains nicotine, which is addictive. Smoking it can cause health problems. (7 marks)

2. Characteristic — **A feature of an organism.**
   Offspring — **The children of a living thing.**
   Variable — **A factor in an experiment that you can control, change or measure.**
   Drug — **A substance that changes how the body works.**
   (3 marks for all lines drawn correctly, otherwise 2 marks for two lines drawn correctly and 1 mark for one line drawn correctly)

3. a) **Micro**-organism: an extremely small **living** thing, e.g. bacteria. (2 marks)
   b) **Inheritance**: when characteristics get passed on from a **parent** to its offspring. (2 marks)
   c) **Circulatory** system: the system that transports substances around the body in the **blood**. (2 marks)

Key Diagrams

4. **Artery**: carries blood away from the heart.
   Vein: carries blood back to the heart.
   Capillary: where substances move in and out of the blood.
   (3 marks)

Now Try These

5. **Switches** can control the flow of electricity in a circuit. (1 mark)

6. The closer a **light** source is to an object, the **larger** the object's shadow. (2 marks)

7. **a line graph** (1 mark)

8. **Variation** (1 mark)

9. **False**
   True
   True (3 marks)

10. E.g. **because they were more likely to reach higher branches on trees and so eat more leaves**. (1 mark)

11. a) **Mammals** (1 mark)
    b) **Birds** (1 mark)
    c) **Fish** (1 mark)

12. The blood carries **oxygen** (from the air), **nutrients** (from food) and water all around the body. Our body parts use them, and produce **waste** substances. The blood carries these substances to the **lungs** and kidneys to be removed. (4 marks)

13. Any two from e.g. **they have thin needle leaves that stop them losing water / they have fleshy stems that store water / they have long roots that find as much water as possible in the ground** (2 marks)

14. Any three from: e.g. **tables / line graphs / scatter graphs / bar charts / diagrams / keys** (3 marks)

15. **Nicotine** (1 mark)

16. Light rays travel in **straight** lines, and mirrors reflect light rays back at the same **angle**. Mirrors can be useful for seeing **around** objects — for example, submarines use **periscopes** (which have two mirrors) to see above water. (4 marks)

17. E.g. **animals can't make their own food, but plants can. / Animals can move around, but plants are fixed in the ground.** (2 marks)

18. a) **Brighter** (1 mark)
    b) **Brighter** (1 mark)
    c) **Dimmer** (1 mark)